An Angel Told Mary About

The Bible tells us about God's plan for Jesus to be with us on earth so that we might learn about God's love for us. The Angel Gabriel was sent to tell Mary that God's plan was for her to become the mother of God's only son, Jesus. Mary loved God very much and said yes to God's plan. (Cf. *Lk* 1:26-38)

Question: What was God's plan for Mary? (To become the mother of God's only son, Jesus.)

Activity: Connect and color the letters of the word Mary said to God's wonderful plan.

Mary Helped Her Cousin Elizabeth

Mary learned from Angel Gabriel that her relatives Elizabeth and Zacharias were going to have a son, too. He would be called John. So Mary quickly traveled to Elizabeth's home in order to visit and help her. Elizabeth was filled with joy when Mary arrived. Elizabeth and Mary rejoiced and praised God. (Cf. *Lk* 1:5-23, 39-56)

Question: Who did Mary and Elizabeth praise for the good news about Jesus and John?

Mary and Joseph Traveled to Bethlehem

BETHLEHEM

While Mary and Joseph were waiting for Jesus to be born, the ruler over their country said that everyone in the world had to be counted. So Mary and Joseph traveled to Bethlehem and put their names on the ruler's list. (Cf. *Lk* 2:1-6)

Activity: Draw a line to help Mary and Joseph find a path to Bethlehem.

The Birth of Jesus

Bethlehem was very crowded with travelers when Mary and Joseph arrived. There was no room for them in the inn, so they stayed in a stable (a place to keep animals). While they were there, Jesus was born. Mary wrapped baby Jesus in a blanket and gently laid him down in a manger (a feeding box for farm animals). (Cf. *Lk* 2:6-7)

Question: Whose birthday do we celebrate on Christmas day?

Shepherds Heard the Good News

Joy + Peace!

In the fields not far from Bethlehem, there were some shepherds caring for their sheep. An angel appeared and told them the good news about Jesus' birth. Then more angels came. The shepherds heard them joyfully singing, "Glory to God in the highest and peace to God's people on earth!" (Cf Lk 2:8-14)

Question: What was the good news the angels told the shepherds? (*Jesus is born.*)

Activity: Color the two words that tell us about the celebration of Christmas.

The Shepherds Visited Baby Jesus

The shepherds were amazed by the angels. They hurried to Bethlehem. There they found Mary and Joseph with Jesus lying in the manger. Then, the shepherds hurried home and told the good news to others. They praised God for everything they had heard and seen that night. (Cf. *Lk* 2:15-20)

Activity: Connect the numbers that show the path through the fields to the manger in Bethlehem.

The Wise Men Visited Baby Jesus

Wise Men who had traveled from a faraway place came to Bethlehem. They were helped by a bright shining star that showed them the way. The Wise Men were very happy when they found Jesus, Mary, and Joseph. After praising and giving Jesus gifts, they traveled back to where they lived. (Cf. *Mt* 2:1-17)

Discussion: What helped the Wise Men find their way to Bethlehem? What kind of animal did they use to travel? What did they do when they found Jesus, Mary, and Joseph?

Activity: Color the star that helped the Wise Men find Bethlehem.

Jesus Grew Up in Nazareth

Jesus lived with his family in the town of Nazareth. The Bible says that the child Jesus grew and became strong, that he was very wise, and that God was very happy with him. (Cf. *Lk* 2:40) The Bible also says that Jesus obeyed his parents, Mary and Joseph. (Cf. *Lk* 2:51)

Discussion: Do you obey your parent(s)? In what ways do you help at home?

Jesus Taught the People About God's Love

When Jesus grew up he began his work of teaching the people about God. He traveled to cities and towns and spoke to many people about God's love for them. The Bible tells us that Jesus "went about doing good." [*Acts* 10:38] Jesus also invited special friends to travel with him and learn about loving others.

Discussion: Jesus told us to love one another. How do you show love at home to your family? How do you show love when playing with your friends?

Activity: Color the picture of Jesus.

Jesus Fed the Hungry

One day when many people were following Jesus and listening to his teaching, he asked his friends where they could buy bread to feed the hungry people. They told Jesus there wasn't enough money to buy food for all the people.

Then one of Jesus' friends told him about a young boy who had five loaves and two fishes, but said that would not be enough food to feed so many people. Jesus told his friends to tell all the people to sit down on the grass anyway. Jesus took the fishes and loaves of bread which the young boy had offered and gave thanks to God, the Father. Then Jesus began passing the loaves and fishes around to the people.

The people ate as much as they wanted and were filled. Afterward, there was still a lot of food left over. The people were amazed that Jesus fed so many people with just the few fishes and loaves of bread that he had received from the young boy. (Cf. *Jn* 6:1-14)

Jesus often did wonderful things for people because he loved them. In this story, Jesus fed the hungry people with the help of a young boy who had food to share. Jesus often asks those who are his friends to help him to help others. We are Jesus' friends. We can share what we have with others. We can be Jesus' helpers.

Discussion: • How do you feel when others share with you?
• What could you share with your brothers, sisters, or your friends?
• How do you feel when you share with others?

Jesus Welcomed Children

Jesus often spent many hours talking to people about God's love for them and how they could show love for one another. Often very large crowds of people gathered to see Jesus and to hear him talk. Many times parents took their children to see and listen to Jesus.

One day when Jesus finished talking, some children ran up close to him. They wanted to see his loving smile and listen to him. Some grown-up friends of Jesus, however, told the children that Jesus was very tired and that they should go away.

But in a kind and gentle voice Jesus said, "Let the children come to me." He then stretched out his hands to the children and welcomed them to come close to him. Smiling, Jesus blessed the children and told them that he would never be too tired for them. Jesus wanted to be their friend. (Cf. *Mt* 19:13-15; *Lk* 18:15-17)

Discussion: • What did Jesus do to show the children that he welcomed them? (*He reached his hands out to them, smiled, and blessed them.*)
   • What do the words "to bless someone" mean? (*To wish that God take care of them and that good things happen to them.*)
   • How can we show that we are friends of Jesus? (*By being kind and helpful to others.*)

Activity: Draw a picture of yourself next to Jesus.

Jesus Taught Us How to Pray

**Our Father, who art in heaven
hallowed be Thy name;**
(God is very special. We praise him!)

**Thy kingdom come;
Thy will be done on earth as it is in heaven.**
(We should obey God's laws.)

Give us this day our daily bread;
(We ask God to give us what we need.)

**and forgive us our trespasses
as we forgive those who trespass against us;**
*(God forgives us when we are sorry.
We should forgive others, too.)*

**and lead us not into temptation,
but deliver us from evil. Amen.**
*(We ask God to help us to be good
and to protect us.)*

(Cf. *Mt* 6:9-13)

Jesus prayed often — sometimes alone and sometimes with friends. Jesus wants us to pray and gave us a special prayer to teach us how to pray. The prayer Jesus taught us is called the Lord's Prayer or Our Father and it is said by Christians (those who believe in Jesus) all over the world.

Discussion: How do you pray at church? At school? At home? When you are alone?

The Good Shepherd

In one of his many stories in the Bible, Jesus tells us about a good shepherd. Jesus says that a good shepherd is one who takes care of his sheep. The sheep hear the voice of the good shepherd as he calls his sheep by name. The sheep follow the good shepherd because they know his voice and trust him. The good shepherd loves his sheep and protects them from danger. (Cf. *Jn* 10: 3-5)

Discussion: We are like the sheep in this story and Jesus is like our good shepherd. Jesus knows us by name. We listen to the words of Jesus from the Bible. Jesus loves us and cares about us. Jesus wants us to be safe and happy.

Activity: Number the sheep and color the picture.

The Good Samaritan

There was once a man who was traveling from a big city to a small town when robbers attacked him, beat him, and then stole everything he had. The man was left badly hurt.

A grown-up happened to be walking down the same road, but when he saw the man hurt, and lying there, he just went right by.

Later, a second grown-up came by, looked at the man who was hurt and also kept walking.

Then, a third grown-up came down the road. When he saw the man who was hurt, he stopped and went over to him. The third grown-up washed and bandaged the injured man's wounds and then took him to an inn and cared for him.

The next morning, the third grown-up gave money to the owner of the inn and asked him to take care of the injured man. The grown-up also promised that if more money was needed, he would pay the owner upon his return trip to the inn.

After telling this story, Jesus asked the people, "Which of the three grown-ups showed love to the man who was robbed and beaten?" (Cf. *Lk* 10: 25-37)

Discussion: • Jesus often told stories to teach people how to show love and concern for others. What is the answer to the question Jesus asked in this story? (*The third grown-up who was kind and helpful was the one who showed love.*)
• How can you be kind and helpful to your playmates?

Activity: Color every space that has a heart to discover the hidden word that Jesus was talking about in this story.

Thank You, God!

One day while Jesus was going into a village, he met ten sick people who asked him to heal them (take away their sickness and make them well). Jesus told them to go have the religious leader look at them. On the way, the ten people were healed. When one of the ten saw that he was healed, he came back praising God and thanking Jesus. Then Jesus asked, "There were ten people who were healed; where are the other nine?" (Cf. *Lk* 17:11-19)

Discussion: • What is Jesus telling us in this story? (*To remember to say thank you.*)
• For what would you like to thank God?

Jesus traveled to many towns and cities to teach people about God. Jesus showed people that he loved them by helping people who were sick, people who could not walk, and people who could not see. Jesus was a good helper. Jesus asks us to be good helpers, too.

Discussion: How are you a good helper at home? At school? At play with your friends?

Activity: Decorate the picture.

Jesus Rode into Jerusalem

HOSANNA!

Jesus traveled throughout the country helping people and telling them about God's love for them. One day when Jesus rode into the city of Jerusalem on a donkey, crowds of people spread their coats on the road in front of him, while others cut branches and spread them on the road. The people were so happy to see him. They cheered and shouted, **HOSANNA!** (*Praise be to God!*) (Cf. *Mt* 21:1-11)

Question: What did the people shout when Jesus rode into the city on a donkey?

Activity: Trace the letters of the word the people shouted.

Holy Thursday

Jesus shared a special supper with his friends. Jesus told his friends that he loved them and he wanted them *to love one another*. Then Jesus washed the feet of his friends as an example of love and service. (The roads were very dusty and dirty in those days.) Jesus said that when they showed love to others, everyone would know that they were his friends. (Cf. *Jn* 13:34-35)

It was during this meal that Jesus shared with his friends the greatest sign of love and friendship – the gift of himself through the bread and wine he blessed. Then Jesus told his friends: "Do this in memory of me" (*Lk* 22:19). Since that time, Christians all over the world continue to receive the gift of Jesus in Holy Communion.

Discussion: • What does Jesus ask his friends to do? (*To show love for others.*)
• How do you show love for your family and friends?
• What do we call the great gift of love that Jesus gave us? (Holy Communion.)

Activity: Color the very important words Jesus told us.

Good Friday

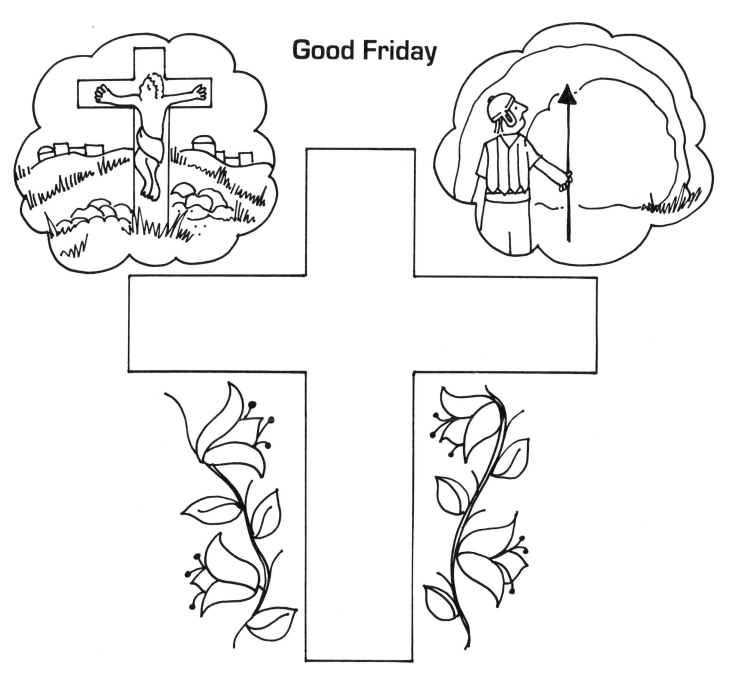

Some people were not friends of Jesus. They did not believe that Jesus was God's son. They did not want to listen to Jesus' teachings. They arranged with the rulers to have Jesus suffer and die on a cross. Afterwards, Jesus was buried in a guarded tomb.

Jesus' friends felt very sad. They thought Jesus would never come back, but as promised, "God raised him from the dead" (Acts 13:30). That is why we celebrate the good news of Jesus' return on Easter.

Since that Good Friday the cross is used in homes, churches, schools, and in jewelry to show that people believe in the risen Jesus and to remember his love for us.

Discussion: We know that sometimes people get hurt, become sick, have accidents, and that someday everyone will die. We do not always understand how or why bad things happen, especially to good people. But, as friends of Jesus, we believe that no matter what happens during our life, "We still hope in God who is our help." (Cf. Ps 33:20). God cares about us and someday will make everything all right because God loves us and keeps promises.

Activity: Decorate the cross that reminds us of Jesus.

Easter Sunday

Alleluia!

On the third day after Jesus died, the most wonderful thing happened! His friends discovered that the tomb where Jesus had been buried was empty. Jesus was alive again, and he returned to his friends. Jesus had not left them. Jesus had kept his promise. Easter is a happy day! Easter is a day to celebrate the new life of Jesus! Easter is a day to sing and rejoice! Alleluia, Alleluia!

Discussion: Why are we happy at Easter?

Activity: Color the letters of the word we use on Easter to praise God for the new life of Jesus.

Jesus Visited His Friends

During the weeks following Easter, the risen Jesus visited his friends several times. One day, Jesus went to the seashore and did a wonderful thing for his friends who had not caught any fish all night. Jesus told them where to throw their net. Suddenly, their net was filled with many, many fish. Peter, one of Jesus' friends, dragged the net of fish to the shore. Then Jesus had breakfast of fried fish and bread with his friends. (Cf. *Jn* 21:1-14)

Activity: Draw more fish in Peter's net.

Love God and love one another, as I have loved you.

The risen Jesus told his disciples (special friends) to go to all the people in the world and teach them, so that they might become Jesus' friends, too. Jesus wants everyone to belong to God's family through Baptism in the name of the Father, Son, and Holy Spirit. Jesus also told his friends that they would never be alone because his Spirit would always be in their hearts. (Cf. *Mt* 28:19-20)

Discussion: What message does Jesus want everyone in the world to hear and obey?

Activity: Color the words of Jesus' message.

Jesus Returned to Heaven

The Bible tells us that the risen Jesus spent time on earth after Easter. He visited his friends, ate with them, and continued to teach them about God. When it was time for Jesus to return to God in heaven, he gathered his friends. Jesus raised his hands and blessed them. And then, Jesus was gone. (Cf.*Acts* 1:3, 9)

Discussion: Where did Jesus go? (*To God in heaven.*) Can we see God or Heaven? (*No, not now, but someday we hope to see and be with God in heaven.*)

Jesus is With Us

When the risen Jesus went to heaven, he did not leave us alone. Jesus lives in the hearts of everyone who loves him. (Cf *Jn* 14:15-21) Jesus is like a lighted candle that guides us. Jesus' words tell us to love God and to love one another. Whenever we see a candle burning, it can help us think about Jesus.

Question: What do Jesus' words tell us? [*To love God and to love one another.*]

Activity: Color the burning candle that helps us to think about Jesus.